Tashi

www.TheTashiChronicles.com

Dedication

To **Donna**, the Love of My Life.
The best thing that ever happened to me
and the Greatest "Dog Mom" ever.
To **Sashi** (October 21, 2011 – November 20, 2020)
Like the 'daughter' I never had and the Source
of My Inspiration for this Book.

Love Always, Philip

THE TASHI CHRONICLES

Tails from Tibet

LEADERSHIP LESSONS
FOR YOUNG LIVES

Written by Philip Martin

Illustrated by Beata Banach

ISBN-13 978-1-949033-96-0 (paperback)
ISBN-13 978-1-949033-97-7 (hardcover)
ISBN-13 978-1-949033-98-4 (ebook)

CONTENTS

www.TheTashiChronicles.com

Tails from Tibet

LEADERSHIP LESSONS
FOR YOUNG LIVES

CHAPTER 1
The Journey Begins

Tashi is a tan and white Tibetan Terrier. She is just sixteen months old and lives in a beautiful home and wonderful community with her adopted parents. Her name means "good fortune" in the Tibetan language — and Tashi certainly knows how remarkable her life is already.

One day Tashi overhears her parents talking about a family tree and she wonders what this means. Tashi is still a young pup and new to her family. She wants to know as much about them as possible, especially where she comes from.

Tashi has an older sister named Sashi who is eight-years-old. Tashi notices that Sashi looks just like her, except her coat is black and white. Both Sashi and Tashi have soft hair hanging down over their eyes and long, draping hair that goes to the ground. Their coats are silky, soft, and wavy and the hair appears to almost float as they trot around.

"Sashi, what is a family tree?" asks little Tashi. "Is there one in our backyard? Have we seen one on our walks?"

Sashi lets out a pup laugh. "Oh, Tashi, that is really cute! A family tree refers to a person's or a pup's heritage or bloodline. It's who our ancestors are and where we come from."

"Oh, okay! That makes sense!" exclaims Tashi. "I always wondered why you and I look so much alike, yet so different from other dogs."

"That's a *paw*-some observation, Tashi," replies Sashi. "We have a double-coat that helps keep us warm in the winter and cool in the summer. Our ancestors come from villages in the country of Tibet, which is far away from here and way up in the Himalayan Mountains."

"Wow!" exclaims Tashi. "That is so amazing! Can you tell me more?"

"Absolutely," continues Sashi, "the hair over our eyes protects us from the fierce winds, snow, and cold. The small pads on our feet help us walk in the snow, just like doggie snowshoes. We are also excellent guard dogs and can climb mountains. We are very agile."

"I can't believe it! I can climb mountains and guard the house, too? It is no wonder we look and move the way we do!"

"Yes, Tashi, that is our heritage and where we come from. It is also why we act the way we do and possess the talents we have. It makes us very different from other dogs!"

"Please tell me more?" begs little Tashi.

"I'll do something better," says Sashi, "I'll show you!"

Just then, a giant golden eagle sweeps in and lands right between the pups. Tashi's eyes are as big as frisbees.

"Tashi," says Sashi, "this is my friend, Yeshe. Yeshe has watched over me for years, and we have shared many wonderful adventures together. I have learned a lot from him."

"Hello, Yeshe. That is a very unusual name," says Tashi. "What does it mean? I am eager to learn. Will you take me on an adventure, too? Where will we go? How do we get there?"

Sashi chuckles. "So many questions, little one. Be patient, and you will find the answers."

Yeshe introduces himself. "Hello, little pup. My name is Yeshe. It means 'Wise One,' and my ancestors also came from Tibet. I would love to take you on one of our magical journeys. It is important to understand where you come from and why you are the way you are. Would you like to take a journey to your homeland of Tibet?"

"Really!" Tashi exclaims, jumping around with excitement. "But I thought Tibet was very far away?"

Yeshe remarks, "It is, Tashi, very far away, but just like you and Sashi have special gifts to help you do amazing things in life, so do I. Now, jump onto the back of my wings — both of you — and let's go see where you come from."

CHAPTER 2
It starts with Trust

"I'm not sure about this," Tashi says softly, unsure of what Yeshe suggests. "Is this safe? I'm a dog, not a bird."

"Yes, Tashi, it is safe. I've done this many times before," says Sashi soothingly. "Yeshe won't let anything bad happen to us. The only way to get to see new things and experience new adventures is to be brave and fearless. You become brave by doing things outside your comfort zone."

"But what if we fall? Aren't we going to be high in the sky? I'm used to sniffing the ground, not the clouds!" Tashi persists.

"I'm glad you're cautious, but as long as you follow Yeshe's instructions, you'll be fine. Learning to trust was hard for me, but it gets easier every time. Courage, like trust, is grown by doing new and, sometimes, scary things. You never know what you can do until you try."

Still full of questions, Tashi continues to ask, "Won't Mom and Dad miss us? Should we tell them where we're going? Can we pack some snacks? Won't I need a winter coat?"

"Tashi, I already told them we were going on an adventure, you just ate, and you're wearing your coat! Soon you'll see that you already have everything you need. Yeshe and I have done this many times before, and I am your older sister, so I will take excellent care of you. You can hold my paw if that makes you feel safer."

"You need not worry, Tashi," says Yeshe. "I'm a golden eagle, and flying is what I do. Like you and Sashi are guard dogs up in the Himalayas and companions to the monks, I am a majestic bird representing freedom, strength, and loyalty. I'm not a chicken," Yeshe adds with a chuckle.

Sashi bursts out laughing, "I should say not! Chickens don't even fly because well … they're chicken!"

Yeshe bows his head and spreads his giant, golden wings, signaling the pups to climb aboard. "Tashi, close your eyes and count to three."

Tashi begins, "One, two, two-and-a-half, two-and three-quarters, hey, what's a monk?"

Exhausted by questions, Sashi says, "You have to trust me and just count to three already."

"Three!" exclaims Tashi. And with that, the two pups are swept up onto Yeshe's wings, ready for the flight of their life.

CHAPTER 3
Learning Obedience

s the three friends soar over the land and sea, Tashi is in amazement at the scenery below. "Wow, this is awesome, Sashi. Thank you for bringing me, and for making me open my eyes and look down."

"You're very welcome, sister, but please, when we land, do not run off. You will see and smell many new things, but it is very important that you stay nearby and listen to Yeshe and me. Not everything new is going to be good," Sashi reminds her sister.

Just then, the clouds parted and Yeshe exclaims, "Prepare for landing, ladies!"

The girls hold onto Yeshe's majestic wings for three final flaps, cresting just above a mountain and freefalling gracefully to the ground. Yeshe lands on a plateau in the beautiful country of Tibet, taking a few steps to slow his momentum and keep his balance with the dogs aboard.

The beauty of the land seemed to render Tashi speechless, but only for a moment. Yeshe lowers his head and wings for the two dogs to climb off.

"Wonderful flight, Yeshe. You are a very good pilot," remarks Sashi.

As they get re-oriented after the magical flight, Yeshe turns to the two dogs and says, "My plan is to hike along these mountain tops and eventually get to the special region known as the Lost Valley. It is said to be the specific area where your ancestors actually came from."

Tashi, overwhelmed by the new sights and smells, spots a strange group of animals grazing on the grass and darts off to take a closer look. Before she could reach the animals, Sashi cries out, "Stop, Tashi! Remember what I said about running off?"

"But, Sashi. I have never seen those things before," Tashi whines. "What are they, anyway?"

"They are goats, Tashi, and they are common in Tibet and in America, just not at our house. Although you want to wander, I have to insist that you do as we say. It is far too dangerous to explore on your own."

"Okay, can we go see them, please? I want a closer look," Tashi begs.

So, the two dogs trotted over for a closer look as Yeshe flies overhead. Yeshe loves the vastness of the mountains in Tibet and the clean, cool air. He climbs as high as he can and circles back down to just a few feet above the girls.

"I won't be very far away from you," Yeshe calls to the pups. "The crisp air here is beautiful, and I love soaring in the wind. I'll keep an eagle's eye on you from above."

As the two girls inch closer to the goats, Sashi says, "Not too close, Tashi. We want to look, but not disturb them. They are not an enemy; however, they are not our friend, either. We must respect their space so as not to threaten them."

"They're so very funny looking," Tashi remarks to Sashi. "Why do some have horns and some don't? Why are they all different colors? Why are they different sizes?"

"You sure do like to ask questions, Tashi. The boy goats have horns and the girl goats do not. The small goats are a different breed than the tall goats. It's kind-of like the difference between us and a Beagle or Labradoodle: we are all dogs, but we all do not look the same. Now let's go. There is a lot to see."

Sashi leads little Tashi onto a trail towards the village while their good friend, Yeshe, joyfully and gracefully circles overhead.

Looking up in the sky, Tashi jokes to Sashi, "Yeshe is like one of us with a good bone or having our back scratched or after a belly rub — happy, relaxed, and joyful."

CHAPTER 4
Being Courageous

Suddenly, Yeshe sounds an alarm from above. Out of nowhere, a jackal jumps into the path of Sashi and Tashi.

Tashi is so startled she jumps back, slips, and falls off the rocks. The jackal turns to chase after Tashi.

Sashi immediately positions herself between Tashi and the jackal, standing firm and barking a warning for the stranger to stay away.

At the same time, Yeshe swoops down and confronts the menacing jackal. The jackal, realizing that he cannot win this fight, turns and runs away.

"Sashi!" cries Tashi. "What was that? It looks like a very scary and mean creature!" Tashi is shaken up — she has only ever met friendly animals before this. "It growled at me and chased me! It looked like it wanted to bite me with its big teeth!"

Yeshe and Sashi immediately begin comforting Tashi. "I am so sorry that happened, Tashi. The world has some scary things, and we need to be ready to confront them and defend our friends from them."

"I'm sorry I didn't warn you both sooner," says Yeshe. "Tashi, a jackal is a cross between a wolf and a dog. It lives in these mountains, not in a house like you and Sashi. He must have been out hunting for dinner and we startled him hiding in the rocks. I am so thankful you weren't far from each other."

Tashi is still shaking and even whimpering from being so scared.

"Let me tell you a story about the first time I was startled by an animal," begins Sashi. "It was a beautiful day in the woods back home, much like today. The crickets were chirping and birds were singing. I chased a rabbit into a clover patch and then heard rustling in the bushes. I thought it must be another rabbit, but I was sadly mistaken. It was a red fox!"

"What did you do? How did you get away? Did you panic like I did here?" asks Tashi.

"Yes, Tashi. I did all of those things, and I was lucky that he was more into rabbits than dogs. I could have been his lunch! I didn't have a big sister to defend me and a golden eagle up above so all I could do was get in my 'power' stance, puff up my chest, make the meanest face I could, and growl loudly."

"Did it work?" Tashi asks in full awe of Sashi's bravery.

"That time, just like this time, it did work, but it may not always. Animals in the wild do not have bowls of food and water provided to them. They do not have soft, comfy beds to lie on and balls to chase. When we are out in the world, we are visiting someone else's home and environment. Many animals live in the wild and the only defense we have are courage and bravery — along with each other," Sashi explains.

"I see why I need to stay close to my friends and stand my ground when something unexpected or scary happens," says Tashi. "Thank you both for teaching me how to be courageous and brave. I feel so much better now after learning what to do and how to be when I am frightened. You turned a potentially bad experience into a great learning opportunity. I feel so much better now. I bet that jackal is glad he didn't have to deal with Yeshe."

"Come on, you two," says Yeshe, "it's time to continue our journey. We need to keep moving. I want you both to see the Lost Valley. It will be dark soon."

CHAPTER 5

Perseverance is Important

s the three companions continue their journey, they travel down the rocky terrain and come to a mountain stream directly in their path. The stream is vast and the water is moving quickly.

They have come too far to turn back and need to continue this adventure so they can hopefully find the Lost Valley. Sashi looks around for the quickest way to cross. She starts out across the rocks, but the water is far too deep and the current too swift. Meanwhile, Tashi paces on the shore, looking for an alternative route.

"Sashi, Sashi! Come this way!" exclaims Tashi as she starts climbing onto a downed tree limb lying in the water. "I think we can make it if we go this way!"

Sashi calls out to Yeshe, "Please scout ahead and see if this is a good solution."

"This tree limb won't work. It stops halfway across," Yeshe confirms. "But I see one further downstream that might work. Why don't you practice your footing first and see if you both feel you have the balance to make it the whole way across? You may need to leap off to avoid the water, but I will keep an eye on you."

"Thanks, Yeshe," exclaims Sashi. "Tashi, great job identifying the tree limb as a solution. Let's practice putting our paws onto one on the ground so we can see how to balance better. It will build our confidence."

"You got it, Sashi! I always wanted to try this! I've seen our neighbor dog, Angel, a Border Collie, walk across a beam in the dog park many times," says Tashi. "It looked like fun. I bet I can do it!"

"That's great to have a positive attitude, Tashi, but practice is very important — and practice makes perfect. So let's try this a couple of times before we venture across the stream."

Tashi and Sashi both take turns jumping on and off the downed tree. Once they are comfortable, they try balancing and walking a few feet at a time, each time going a little further. They even practice going backward.

Suddenly, Tashi loses her grip and falls off the side of the tree limb, splashing into the stream.

Defeated, she pouts as she climbs out of the water. "I just can't do this, Sashi, it is much harder than I thought. I am sorry, but I just can't. Back home my friend Angel makes all this agility stuff look so easy, but it's not easy. It is very hard."

Sashi says, "Do you smell that strange aroma? And what is the strange sound I hear? That's what's waiting on the other side."

"I do smell it, Sashi. What is it? And that sound! It is pretty eerie, but really soothing too."

"The only way to find out is to keep going. So, let's try a few more times. Falling off is normal. You get better every time you get up and try again. I promise."

After a few more attempts, Sashi exclaims, "Look at you, Tashi! You've got it! Now let's go cross this stream."

"This reminds me of a joke," Yeshe says from above. "Why did the chicken cross the road?"

"To get to the other side!" exclaims Sashi.

The golden eagle laughs so hard he almost falls from the sky.

Little Tashi is just taking it all in and feeling a bit overwhelmed while also having the time of her life!

And with that, the dogs run to the large tree limb that goes the whole way across the stream and they begin crossing it. At the very end, they make a giant leap, almost too soon — not quite far enough to get across — but then each pup instinctively does a special little "kick" up in the air that propels her a bit further. It's a trait unique to the Tibetan Terriers. And they make it!

The pups are so excited and proud of their big accomplishment! Landing safely on the other side of the stream, Sashi is relieved.

"Wow! We did it!" exclaims Tashi.

"You certainly did," says Yeshe, "great job persevering and conquering the obstacle! You both worked so well together — practicing and helping one another — and you never gave up!"

Yeshe adds, "Watching all of this from up above has been thrilling! You two were fantastic! On we go. Let's check out those strange smells and that unusual sound. Where were they coming from?"

"I think I see a temple up ahead."

CHAPTER 6
Patience is Admirable

As the pups continue their trek, Sashi and Tashi are still talking back and forth, excited about crossing the stream.

"I can't believe we did that, Sashi!" Tashi stops and turns to her sister. "This adventure is just incredible! I am learning and seeing so much. Thank you so much for mentoring me until I listened and followed your lead."

"You are so welcome, Tashi, that is how I learned to lead. Somebody else taught me and I was open to trust and to learn. The same thing happened to Yeshe. Someday you'll get the opportunity to teach another pup just like I am teaching you. There might be a lot of others someday who would like to learn from you. That's the meaning of life, and that's what makes a good life have purpose. Now, let's keep moving; there's a whole lot more to see and do!"

The dogs follow Yeshe and he guides them toward the unusual aroma and strange sound, both of which are becoming stronger.

"Oh, that smells good, Sashi! What is that?"

"What do you smell, Tashi? Describe what it smells like to you."

"It smells like a campfire, but with flowers! I like the smell, but I wouldn't want to eat it."

Continuing on, the trio comes into a clearing where they see the most beautiful temple with a courtyard. It is the most unusual structure Tashi has ever seen. In the courtyard, there are two Buddhist monks and two dogs who look just like Sashi and Tashi but their haircut is different and you cannot see their eyes with the hair hanging down over their face. But Sashi and Tashi know they are the same. The dogs are sitting so calmly and are very attentive.

"Sashi, look!" Tashi exclaims. "There are dogs just like us! But look how well behaved they are. They stay right by their humans — and they don't even have a fence or a leash."

"That's right, Tashi," explains Sashi, "those are the Tibetan Terriers of the monks and the unusual aroma you smell is the incense they burn daily at the temple."

"Oh, so that's a monk", replies Tashi. "Sashi, why do they burn incense?"

"It's part of their ritual, Tashi, and the dogs you see are their trusted companions. For more than two thousand years, Tibetan Terriers like us have lived among the Buddhist monks at their temples. They are wonderful companions to the monks. The Tibetan Mastiffs, quite a bit larger than we are and another of our ancestors, have been guard dogs at the temples, vigilantly guarding the monastery entrances and chasing away intruders."

Yeshe calls out, "I have been wanting to show you both the Lost Valley, which is the part of Tibet where your ancestors came from. It is called that because an earthquake destroyed the major road that allowed access to the valley in the fourteenth century. Oh, and by the way, for several centuries, Tibetan Terriers have been considered good luck charms."

Tashi is intrigued by the two dogs nearby sitting with the Monks. "They sure are paying attention and listening to the Monks."

"Yes, Tashi, they are extremely well-trained and obedient. They are also patient and only act on the command of the monks. The monks and people in the villages actually refer to the dogs like you as 'Little People.'"

Tashi exclaims, "That is so cool! Like Little People! No wonder people see us as so different from other dogs!"

"Can we go meet them? After all, we are related, right? Aren't they part of our family tree and the reason we flew all the way across the world?" asks Tashi excitedly.

"Yes, they are Tashi, but they are working, and we do not want to disturb them. It's best to just observe them. I wanted you to see them in their natural habitat. Besides, we really don't have time right now as we need to continue our journey."

"Okay, well, if we can't see our cousins, can we at least find something for dinner? I'm starving from all the action today!"

"I'm on it!" calls out Yeshe as he swoops down with a large fish in his talons.

"Hurray!" barks Tashi. "Fish sticks! My favorite!"

CHAPTER 7
The Wonders of Curiosity

After finishing their delicious feast of fresh fish, the dogs and Yeshe take a rest break. Yeshe adds, "Tashi, in the same way the two dogs with the monks were very patient, I, too, had to be very patient as I waited to catch that big fish for our dinner. Learning to be patient is so very important."

While they are resting, they once again hear an extraordinary and unusual sound coming from the direction of the temple.

"What is that, Sashi? You showed me what the smell was, but I never found out about that strange sound? I've never heard anything like that before. What does that noise mean? Is it like a doorbell? Is that how they call their dogs for dinner?"

"I'm not sure what it is, Tashi," says Sashi, "but I do know it's not a gong. This sound is different, almost like a singing noise instead of a single tone. It is very calming, don't you agree?"

"I sure do, it almost has a little echo to it," answers Tashi. "What's a gong?"

"A gong is a big, round hanging metal disc that humans strike with a big baton, and it makes an intense and loud tone that resonates. Monks use them in their ceremonies."

Tashi gets up and begins moving towards the sound. She is curious and has to find out what it is, as does Sashi. Curiosity builds and both pups move toward the temple.

"What is that Yeshe?" asks Sashi. "I have never heard this sound before."

"My dear pups," answers Yeshe, "that is the sound of a Tibetan Singing Bowl. It's a musical instrument used by the monks to bring calmness and peace into their lives."

"It sounds so beautiful. Yeshe, I love the way the echoes seem to go on forever," comments Sashi.

"How do the monks make the bowls sing? How can anything sing when it doesn't have a mouth?" asks Tashi.

"Let me show you, and then you'll understand. I love how you are so curious about a different culture and want to learn more. And I hope you stay very curious your entire life, sweet Tashi."

Yeshe leads the two pups back to the temple courtyard clearing where the monks are now sitting with various metal bowls of different shapes and sizes. The monks hold the bowl in one hand and circle the outside with a stick in their other hand.

"I have never seen anything like that," Sashi is amazed. "The sound is just so unusual, and it's coming from a bowl. The sound makes me so calm and relaxed. I believe I could easily take another nap."

"I wonder if I could do that at home with my water bowl and Yak Cheese stick!" exclaims Tashi.

The two monastery guard dogs sit quietly at the feet of the monks, observing everything and enjoying the soothing sounds of the singing bowls.

"Wow, I am learning so many new things!" exclaims Tashi.

"That's because you are curious, Tashi," says Yeshe. "A curious mind is always open to discovery. Never lose this wonderful trait no matter how old you get."

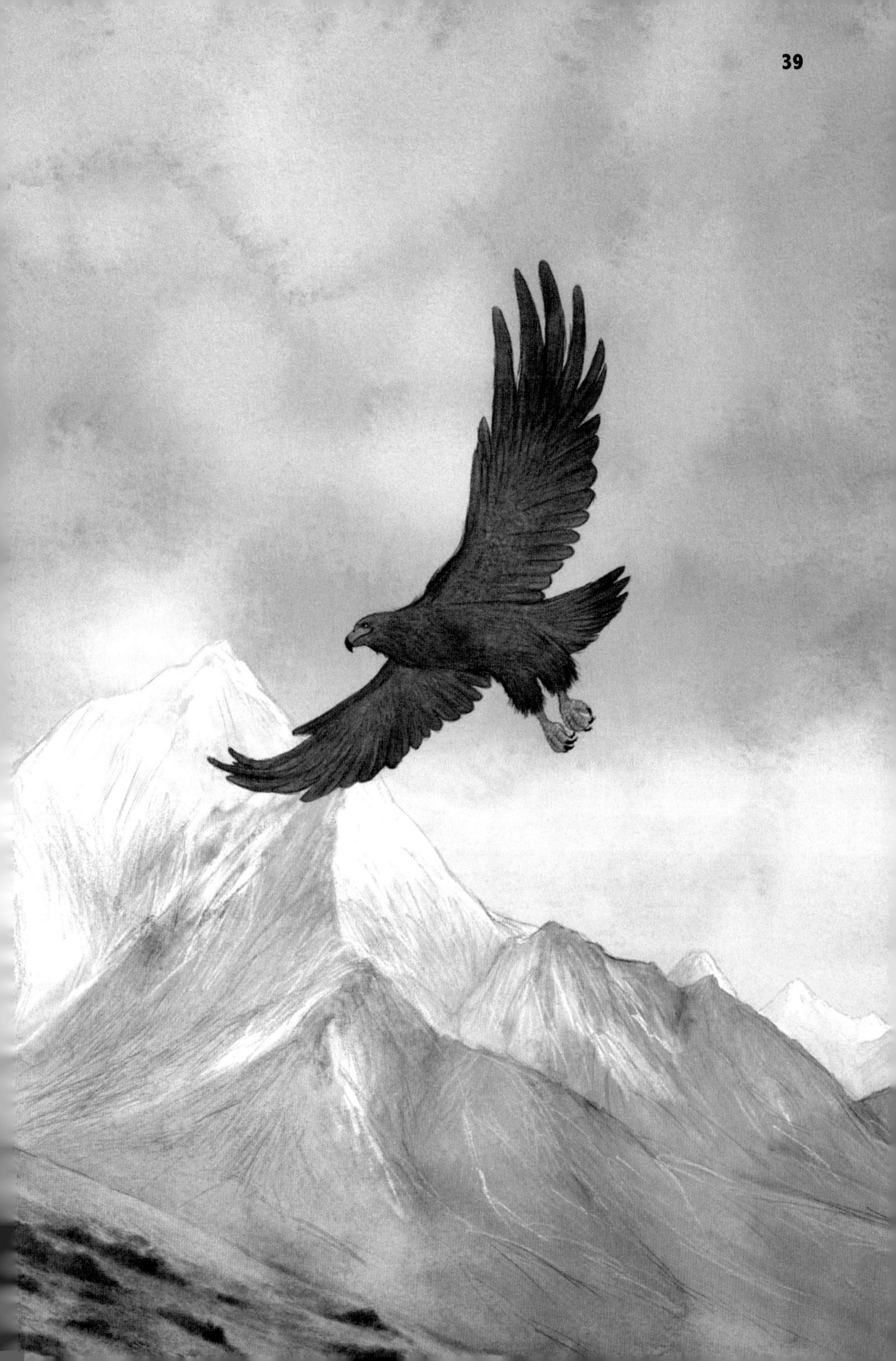

CHAPTER 8
Be Fearless

Deciding it was time to move on, the two dogs walk away from the Temple and meander down the side of the mountain. Yeshe, still keeping an eye on the two dogs, is circling above and remaining in flight. In the distance, Tashi spots a group of animals she had never seen before.

"Sashi, what are they?" Tashi asks. "They look so white and fluffy, like clouds on legs."

Sashi chuckles, "They are sheep, Tashi, and they do look like clouds on legs. People use sheep for many things, but mostly they provide wool. You see, they are fluffy now, but soon they will have their wool coat removed in a process called sheering. Sheering is a fancy name for the buzzcut the sheep receive. The humans collect their curly coats to create textiles and fabrics. Sheep are part of the cycle of life, so they may also be used for food."

"Will we be used for food, Sashi?" Tashi asks with her voice cracking.

"No, Tashi," Sashi says calmingly. "Humans in our country and Tibet employ dogs and pamper dogs, but they do not eat dogs."

"Why are there so many of them? There must be hundreds! Humans sure do need a lot of wool!" Tashi remarks.

"They sure do Tashi, especially in this cold part of the world and in the mountains," Sashi adds.

Just then, Sashi notices a small sheep in the middle of four much larger sheep. Looking around, she does not see the shepherd or the sheepdogs. The larger sheep are picking on the smallest member of the flock. Knowing that teasing and bullying are bad, Sashi moves closer to the flock to assert herself into the conversation, but before she can even say anything, Tashi jumps in between the four large sheep and the small sheep, the one they are picking on.

"Hey, stop that!" Tashi says to the larger sheep. "There is no need to act like that," she continues. The four large sheep are startled by Tashi and her bold remarks. Tashi remembers the "power stance" that Sashi had taught her when the jackal approached them. Tashi gets into her power stance and watches to see what the large sheep will do next.

Sashi is so impressed by watching this and admires Tashi's growth and development in a short time. Her bravery and courage to get in on the action to do what is right make Sashi very proud.

Remembering what Sashi has taught her, Tashi finds her own brave voice, and calling out to the small sheep, she says, "Are you okay, little one?"

"I will be," the little sheep says between sobs. "They were so mean. Thank you for helping me, both of you." Tashi is feeling mighty good about this encounter, but not quite sure what her next move will be.

Coming in on the tail end of the situation, a herding dog calls out in his deep voice, "What is going on here? Is everything all right?"

"It is now. You are here just in time," responds Tashi, "A few of your larger sheep thought about picking on this little guy. When I didn't see you, my sister and I came to the little sheep's aid. My name is Tashi, by the way, and this is my older sister, Sashi. We are from America and on our way to the Lost Valley to see where our ancestors came from."

The sheepdog replies, "Wow! What an incredible trip! We see a lot of your relatives up here in the mountains. Your particular kind is very unusual. Most of the time we see them with the Monks. By the way I am a Himalayan Sheepdog and we come from Nepal. We might even be related."

"You mean you could be on our Family Tree?" asks Tashi.

"Possibly. Wouldn't that be great if we were distant cousins?"

"That would be *paw*-some!" exclaims Tashi.

The sheepdog adds, "My name is Amir. In Nepal, it means 'a born leader.'"

Hearing that, Tashi exclaims, "I want to become a strong leader some day."

Amir says, "Tashi, I know you are learning a lot on your journey that will help you become that leader. Continue to listen

to Sashi and others who are older and wiser and who have had more of life's experiences to share with you."

The handsome sheepdog continues, "Thank you for running interference. I have to get back to work with the flock. Our flock has doubled in size and, while there are four of us, we can't see everything. I am so grateful for your help."

"You're welcome," Tashi and Sashi bark in unison.

"I might like to be a sheepdog some day," calls out Tashi.

Sashi adds, "We will see, little one. We'll talk about that later."

"We must be on our way, but it was very nice to meet you," Sashi adds.

With that, Sashi and Tashi wave farewell and return to their mountain path to continue their journey as Yeshe comes back into sight.

"Great job Tashi," says Yeshe, "you are just a young pup yourself and you stood up for that little sheep. You are fearless, just like your ancestors."

"What a great quality," adds Sashi, "Tashi, for you to be fearless and always try to stand up for what is right. That will help you in so many ways as you get older."

Tashi smiling and so content, says, "Thank you both so much. I feel so lucky to have you in my life."

CHAPTER 9

It's Lonely at the Top

"How's it going, little pup?" Yeshe asks as he soars down from the mountaintop.

"Fantastic!" Tashi barks excitedly. "There has been so much to see and do. This has truly been an amazing adventure. How much longer will we be here?"

"For a while, yet," adds Yeshe. "We still have some daylight and we are so close to the Lost Valley. It is just over that ridge."

"What is it like?" asks Tashi.

"Well, it's a plateau surrounded by incredible peaks of the Himalayan Mountains," Yeshe begins.

"I wasn't asking about that, silly," laughs Tashi. "What is it like to be a golden eagle? I have seen so many new animals and I am truly amazed, but you fascinate me, Yeshe."

"Why thank you, Tashi," Yeshe responds, preening just a little. "Sit down on those rocks and I will perch on this branch. We have been moving ahead of schedule so let's take a break."

Sashi interjects, "I am a little tired too, I must admit, after that encounter with the sheep, a short rest sounds like just what I need."

As Yeshe describes being a golden eagle, Sashi and Tashi lie down on some rocks warmed by the setting sun.

"Golden eagles are like other birds in that we love our companions and nurture our young. Mama eagles are so patient and kind, but extremely protective. The mama eagles not only feed their young, which are called eaglets after they hatch in their giant nests, but they teach the eaglets to fly when they are old enough," Yeshe remarks. "I remember when my mama taught me."

"Is it like learning to sit or stay?" Tashi asks, entirely attentive and focused on Yeshe.

"Not really. It is more like learning to cross that stream. For an eagle, flying is key. We use our wings and the power of flight to defend and protect. It takes a lot of time and practice and more practice to learn to fly," Yeshe continues. "Many times, young eaglets will fall long before they learn to fly. The important thing is to keep on going, just as you did trying to cross that stream. Eagles must fly to survive — and failing or giving up are simply not options."

"Did you fall, Yeshe?" Tashi asks as her sister, Sashi, dozes off for a bit of a nap.

"Of course," responds Yeshe. "Falling is part of flying. But learning to fly is bittersweet. Once an eaglet learns to fly, it is on its own to tackle the world."

"What do you mean, Yeshe?" asks Tashi. "You mean you leave home for good?"

"That's right, Tashi. Eagles are loners, for the most part, and we are not the only birds out there. When we come into contact with birds who are mean or aggressive, we must not surrender, no matter how big they are. When the storms come, we fly above the storm, unlike other birds who find shelter until the storms are over. We can soar as high as 10,000 feet, but it is lonely at the top," Yeshe continues with just a bit of reflection and emotion in his voice.

"At least you have some friends, Yeshe," Tashi says comfortingly. "We will always be your friends."

"I do, pup, and I embrace what I was put on this earth to do.

Just like you and Sashi have your family tree, so do I. And while dogs thrive in packs, eagles were created to soar alone. We are each made for a unique purpose," Yeshe says. "I love being an eagle — and I really love being with you two dogs. By the way, I have learned a lot watching both of you on our journey. It can be lonely at times being the leader — sometimes a leader has to step out away from the others to make a tough decision. That can be lonely, too."

Sashi turns to Tashi and says, "I imagine our new friend, Amir, is lonely at times and has to make hard decisions that make him feel lonely. It is all part of becoming a strong leader. To do what is right, even when it is hard."

"Wow," sighs Tashi. "That is a lot for me to think about."

Yeshe calls out, "Now, let's get ready to press on before it gets too dark. I feel like a storm is coming, so let's get moving."

CHAPTER 10
Journey's Goal Accomplished

*S*ashi and Tashi wake up from their nap and Yeshe gathers the two pups to continue the final portion of their trek to reach the Lost Valley.

As the two dogs trot up over the next ridge, they are captivated by what they now see: the Lost Valley! The view is majestic and even more beautiful than how Yeshe had described it. When they recognize the significance of the Lost Valley as the place where their ancestors came from, it is all so amazing to the two dogs.

As Yeshe circles overhead, proudly looking down at the two pups, Sashi exclaims, "It seems unreal! It feels so sacred. I can sure understand now why so much has been written about it over the years. Tashi, this area is legendary in the Tibetan culture. Very few dogs like us or even humans have ever stood here where we are standing and have seen what we see now!"

Tashi says, "It is very inspirational. It makes me feel so peaceful. It is just breath-taking. It is really hard to describe and almost doesn't seem real."

The fascinating view inspires them to reflect on all they have learned in this fantastic, mystical land as they take it all in. Looking out at the mountains and down into the valley, the realization of where they came from is inspiring. Thinking about what the future holds for them makes the dogs ponder what Life has in store for them.

"Sashi, I understand what a family tree is now and why it is important. I know that I am a Tibetan Terrier through and through. Seeing this enchanting land and all that we have experienced has shown me how our traits and talents define our special breed."

"That's right, Tashi, you trusted Yeshe enough to get on his wings so you could see your ancient homeland with your own eyes. You mastered obedience when you listened and did not wander off to visit the goats. You faced your own fears when the jackal scared you, and you learned how brave and courageous we can be. When we came upon the stream, you showed excellent

problem-solving skills. Through our perseverance, we practiced and practiced until we could get across that stream. You demon-strated patience when we saw the monks. Your curiosity helped us learn about singing bowls. You were empathetic, kind, car-ing, and brave when we defended the little sheep, and, finally, you learned fearlessness from Yeshe as he dis-cussed his life and what it means to often stand alone."

"Wow, I did learn and do a lot. I should be exhausted, but I am just so energized, instead," Tashi says to her sister, puffing up her chest.

"Now it is time for you to take what you have learned and share it with the world. I have a feeling a lot of people will enjoy hearing of your adventures and what they can learn from you and your experiences," Yeshe adds.

"May you never forget this journey and the lessons along the way," Sashi said endearingly to her sister.

Yeshe says, "I am so proud of you, Tashi. But, as I suspected, a storm is coming, and we must head home now. I want to get high up in the air before the rains come. Remember, we eagles fly above the storm; that's where clear skies are."

"Oh Yeshe, just five more minutes," Tashi begs.

"Unfortunately, we do not have five more minutes," Yeshe responds. "Perhaps we can return again someday, but for now, you and Sashi need to jump onto my back and prepare yourselves for flight."

"Tashi, you should thank Yeshe for allowing us this opportunity. He has been a most gracious host," Sashi says to her sister.

"Thank you, Yeshe," Tashi says. "I have had the most wonderful experience. I am ready to climb aboard!"

Yeshe spreads his magnificent golden wings. The pups get into position securely and count to three out loud together just like they had before. This time, however, is so different: little Tashi is not afraid at all.

"Are you ready for lift-off?" Yeshe asks.

"We are all set, captain!" Tashi and Sashi bark together.

"This time, I am going to keep my eyes open for the whole flight. I am not afraid anymore, and I am so excited to fly," Tashi says, wagging her tail.

The two Tibetan Terriers nestle down into Yeshe's wings. Yeshe climbs and climbs until they are well above the incoming storm and gracefully soaring into the clouds, over the mountains and the ocean. Before long, the trio magically arrives safely at the exact spot in the yard where they had taken off before.

The two pups disembark and head toward the door to their home, anxious to get into their beds.

"Goodnight, Yeshe," says Sashi, "You are an excellent friend and such a great teacher. I am so thankful for you."

Tashi turns and yells, "I had a really great time, Yeshe! I can't believe everything I saw and learned! I have a very special family tree, I learned about our rich history, and I know what type of leader I can be some day!"

"You are both welcome," says Yeshe, "and remember, I'm always watching over you and we can think about our next adventure."

As the two tired pups get into their beds, Tashi, exhausted, but almost too excited to sleep, says, "I sure am a lucky dog Sashi."

Just then, a loud, booming voice comes from upstairs, "Hey, you two! Time to go to sleep. It is late."

Tashi, so very tired, looks over at Sashi and whispers, "If Mom and Dad had any idea where we have just been…. I am so glad you are my big sister. Good night, Sashi."

Sashi lovingly replies, "Good night, Tashi. Sweet dreams."

Sashi looks over at Tashi, curled up in her bed, and sees she is already sound asleep.

An Open Letter
To Parents, Grand-Parents, and Older Readers

Like many of you, I had a dog when I was a young boy. Then later in life, in my mid-twenties, I got a long-hair dachshund puppy at eight weeks-old. I raised him and took care of him for thirteen years. When he died, I was heart-broken, and it took me a very long time before I could really think about getting another dog.

Donna had never had a dog. She had a cat who lived a long life. When the cat passed away, we began to think about a dog. I remember Donna saying, "This will be your dog. You'll take care of him. You will walk him." And I said, "I sure will." When we began to look for dogs, I surprisingly learned that during this long, intervening time, I had become highly allergic to dogs. I knew I was very allergic to Donna's cat, but to find out now I had developed allergies to dogs was very disappointing. We stopped looking for a dog for a while. Later, on a business trip, I learned about a dog of a business colleague that I was around for a week and during that time I had not developed any allergies. It was a Tibetan Terrier. I was not familiar with the breed. I told Donna about it over the phone. She did some research and we found that they are hypo-allergenic and that there is no shedding. It turned out that one of the top breeders in the world was about thirty miles from our home.

I mention all this because when we got Sashi, a Tibetan Terrier, who was six months old, she changed our lives. The breeder had planned to keep her show her, but she felt that she was not quite big enough. So the story begins here. Donna and I took this beautiful Tibetan Terrier home. We named her Sashi, which means "The

World" in the Tibetan language. Sashi quickly became "the world" to us. She was like the little daughter that we never had.

Donna and I married late in life and did not have children ourselves, so this addition was even more special and emotional. Sashi, Donna, and I were tremendous together. We took Sashi everywhere and we shared so much together. When she developed a stomach issue, we were totally shocked to learn that she had intestinal cancer. Sashi was about eight and a half years old. The Tibetan Terrier breed often lives to seventeen years or more. Her getting sick so young was what was so hard on us. We worked with an oncologist for treatment over several months, but sadly, Sashi passed away a month after her ninth birthday. We were more than heartbroken.

Many people encouraged us to get another dog, but we just didn't feel that the time was right. We reached out to several breeders to let them know we would be interested in the future, plus all of their dogs were all spoken for. I do believe, as does Donna, that it was partly the spirit of sweet Sashi interceding into our dilemma as well as God having a plan for us. We received a call from one of the breeders who had had a cancellation. We went out to see the puppy in December, and it was love at first sight. So that's how Tashi came to our home. She arrived at the end of December 2020 at nine weeks old. Her name means "Good Luck" in the Tibetan language.

As a part of my grieving and healing, I had several people who suggested that I write some of my thoughts down. That became the genesis of this book. As I began to think about what we were teaching to little Tashi, our new nine-week-old puppy, it was only natural to reflect on all that we had learned from Sashi, and through our teaching and time together with Sashi, I felt that possibly putting that on paper would help young people too. A lot of the things that the puppy was learning are the same things I believe a young boy or young girl could benefit from learning as well.

I read that there are countless Leadership books published each year. I am passionate about the topic of Leadership, and I have felt that there is a void in the book world for Leadership Development for young boys and girls. I also found that as I began to think about specific topics to address, I was drawn upon my formative years at Battle Ground Academy, and especially my wonderful years in Scouting. I became a Boy Scout in Nashville, Tennessee, when I was eleven years old and rose up through the ranks in a tremendous Scout Troop. I attained the rank of Eagle Scout when I was fourteen years old. It was an important part of my development and served as a strong foundation as I continued in life to develop both my leadership skills and other life lessons. I found myself reminiscing over the tenets of the Scout Law: Trustworthy, Loyal, Helpful, Friendly, Courteous, Kind, Obedient, Cheerful, Thrifty, Brave, Clean, and Reverent. So many of these elements seem to apply for both what our little puppy needed to learn, as well as what a young boy or girl needs to learn.

Whether you are a young boy or young girl, or an older brother or sister, a parent or grandparent, I sure hope you enjoy this book, and the lessons that we are sharing throughout the escapades of the two dogs. I am honored to introduce you to Tashi, and to the dearly departed Sashi — these special dogs radically changed my life for the better.

Philip Martin / March 2023

Acknowledgements

The idea for writing this book was born in early 2021 shortly after losing **Sashi**, our dear Tibetan Terrier, to cancer. This book would not have been possible without the unwavering support and encouragement from my wonderful wife, **Donna**. I do also acknowledge our sweet, departed Sashi who was the primary inspiration for the book, and little **Tashi**, our new puppy, who is embarking on her life's journey now.

Reflecting on how I got here, it is important to acknowledge **Sally McGhee** and her wonderful Tibetan Terrier, **Prana**. They live in Colorado. I met them in 2011, and that began what would become a love affair with the Tibetan Terrier breed. In 2012, Donna and I met **Sheryl Schultis** and her **Atisha Kennel** in Virginia, and where we got Sashi at six months old.

Soon we became immersed in the Tibetan Terrier community, both locally and in a broader sense. We met **Margy and Ron Pankicwicz**, who were leading the **Mount Vernon Tibetan Terrier Club** that we also joined. Along the way, the **Tibetan Terrier Club of America** was a big source of knowledge.

The **Leesburg Dog School** has helped us with training. We are very grateful to **Dr. Keith Robbins** and the staff at the **Catoctin Veterinary Clinic** in Leesburg, Virginia, for taking good care of Sashi and Tashi during the past ten years. As Sashi's health began to decline, we were introduced to **Dr. Tony Rusk** and his staff at **The Oncology Service** in Leesburg, who helped us with her cancer treatment. In the months that followed, we met **Dolores Robison** and her **Tidewater Tibetan Terriers Kennel** as we began to explore getting another dog. That is where we met Tashi when she was eight weeks old.

In 2015, I established the **Belmont Dog Lovers Club** in the community where we live. The Club has been a great vehicle for meeting other dog owners and for dogs to get to know one another. We have also been supported by **Canine Carousel**, who kept Sashi and Tashi looking so great, and by **Old Towne Pet Resort** for their Doggy Day Care and Boarding, and our dog walkers from **Woofie's.** I am grateful to **Kim Correnti** at **DogGone Natural** for the advice, food, and supplies over the years.

I am also extremely grateful to **David Dean**, my mentor and a lifelong advisor for the past fifty-one years. It was David who strongly encouraged me to consider writing a book, and who introduced me to **Tracey Jones**, the CEO of **Tremendous Leadership Books**. Regarding the book writing endeavor, I am also grateful to Tracey for her wisdom and advice and for **Anthony Michalski** who spearheaded the editing and the layout. I am also very grateful for **Beata Banach**, an extremely talented artist, living in Poland, who brought the story to life as the Illustrator. Friends and relatives helped also as I worked on the book. I am very grateful to **Mary Campisi**, **Lynda Downey**, **Sean Downey**, **Chang Liu**, **Carol Khalsa**, **Priya Gopalakrishnan**, **Sue Bowers,** and **Kristen Penfield** who made wonderful suggestions and provided helpful feedback.

I am also grateful to **Julie Hindle**, who resides in the UK. She is a noted authority on Tibetan Terriers. She has been very helpful in our training of little Tashi. I am also very grateful to our neighbors, family members, and friends, both locally and afar, who have been so supportive. Many have followed us in the travels and exploits of Sashi and now with little Tashi. Their support and encouragement helped make this book idea a reality.

Lastly, I want to mention the dog friends of both Sashi and Tashi. There are many, and I probably will leave some out inadvertently, but I want to recognize **Ginger**, **Gracie**, **Molly**, **Lola**, **Kharma**, **Gizmo**, **Breezy**, **LeiLei,** **Rosie**, **Milo**, **Toby**, **Romeo**, **Annie**, **Kip**, **Mosby**,

Bentley, Cassius, Angel, Mindy, Belle, Ricky, Winter, Lucy, Ollie, Luna, Julian, Duke, Kili, GracieAnn, and **Jesse**. Each of these dogs has had a role in the socialization, growth, and development of Sashi and Tashi, and have helped to make their lives better. For that I am very grateful.

About the Illustrator

Beata Banach is a professional artist who lives in Lublin, Poland. Since childhood, she has been fascinated and intrigued by art. Beata specializes in watercolors, traditional oils, gouache, and ink. She continues to develop her skills and learn new styles and techniques. Beata strives for excellence and has exquisite attention to detail. She is very responsive and quite pleasant to work with. She received her Masters Degree in Fine Arts in 2018 from the Marie Curie-Sklodowska University in Poland where she majored in traditional easel painting.

Beata can be reached on Instagram at *@beata_paints* and by e-mail at *pinkapple223@gmail.com*.

about the author

Philip Martin is an Executive Coach and Management Consultant. He and his wife, Donna, live in Belmont Country Club in Ashburn, Virginia, with Tashi, their two year-old Tibetan Terrier. He has been an ardent student of Leadership for the past five decades and was exposed to many of these principles at an early age when he was in prep school at Battle Ground Academy and during his years in the Boy Scouts. These served as the foundation for "Tails from Tibet". He and Donna are active in Christian Fellowship Church in Ashburn. Philip has a passion for American History, especially the period of the Civil War. His hobbies include politics, country music, travel, and spending quality time with Donna and Tashi.

He can be reached at *pmartin@thetashichronicles.com.*

www.TheTashiChronicles.com

Made in the USA
Middletown, DE
06 May 2023